This book belongs to

make
believe
ideas

This is the story of a very strange fight,

You can read it day by day or read it at night!

There's something else. Can you guess what?

On every page there's some cheese to spot!

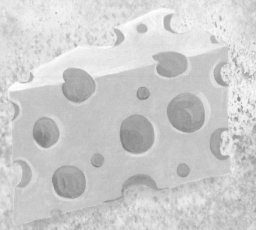

This edition first published in the UK in 2006 by Authentic Media

Copyright © 2006 make believe ideas ltd.

27 Castle Street, Berkhamsted, Herts, HP4 2DW

Text copyright © 2006 Nick and Claire Page

Manufactured in China.

David
and
Goliath

Nick and Claire Page

Illustrations by Nikki Loy

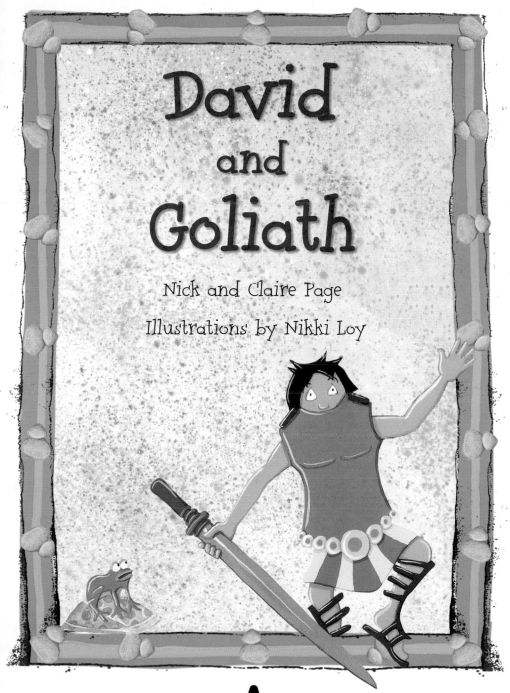

A

Authentic

Long time ago things were bad for Israel,
SCOWL, SNARL, GRUMBLE, GROAN!
At war with the Philistines and not doing well.
SCOWL, SNARL, GRUMBLE, MOAN!

The Philistine army had Goliath on their side,
YIPPEE, HURRAH and WHOOP-DE-DOO!
He was tall as an elephant and almost as wide.
YIPPEE, HURRAH and a big WAH-HOO!

Every evening, every morning,
he would stand on the hill,
BOOM, CLINK, CLANK, TWANG!
Shouting: "Who's strongest here?
Come and fight me if you will!"
BOOM, CLINK, CLANK, BANG!

But everybody hid.
They weren't brave enough to fight.
FLUTTER, RATTLE, SHIVER and SHAKE!
Their knees started knocking
and their faces turned white.
FLUTTER, RATTLE, QUIVER and QUAKE!

9

A boy called David
brought his brothers some food,
YUMMY, SCRUMMY, GOOEY, SLURP!
When he heard Goliath yelling
and being rather rude,
YUMMY, SCRUMMY, GOOEY, BURP!

10

He saw the giant there, so big and tough,
BOOM, CLINK, CLANK, TWANG!
Shouting: "Come and have a go,
if you're brave enough!"
BOOM, CLINK,
CLANK, BANG!

David was amazed. "I'll fight this creep!"
BAH, TUT, SHH, BAH!

"Go home!" said his brothers.

"And look after the sheep."
BAH, TUT, BAA-BAA!

King Saul laughed at David for offering to fight.
CHUCKLE, CHORTLE, GIGGLE, SNARF!
"Goliath is a giant — you're just a little mite."
CHUCKLE, CHORTLE, GIGGLE, LAUGH!

"I'm young, but I've fought with lions and bears."
RIP, POW, BAM, CRASH!
"God helped me then, and he'll do it now, I swear."
RIP, POW, BAM, BASH!

Saul gave him some armour
and a sword in his hand.
CLANK, JANGLE, CLONK, CLASH!
But it was far too heavy – he could hardly stand.
CLANK, JANGLE, BONK, CRASH!

He left the tent and went to a stream.
PLIP, PLUP, PLEPplup, PLIP!
Picked five little stones.
"I'll show that God's supreme."
DRIP, DROP, DREPdrup, DRIP!

That night Goliath stood in front of all his clan,
BOOM, CLINK, CLANK, TWANG!
Shouting: "Come here and face me: giant to man."
BOOM, CLINK, CLANK, BANG!

GO
HOME
PHILISTINES

ISRAEL
WILL
WIN!

Out came David,
with pebbles and a sling.
HA HA, YUK YUK, HERE WE GO!
Goliath laughed so loudly
it made the valleys ring.
HA HA, YUK YUK, HO HO HO!

But David told the giant,
"With God's help, I shall win."
"DAVID, DAVID, HE'S OUR MAN!"
"I don't need heavy armour.
Now let the fight begin."
"IF HE CAN'T DO IT, NO ONE CAN!"

Goliath charged towards him,
his footsteps shook the ground.
STOMP, STOMP, THUMP, GRRR!
With a stone in his sling,
David whirled it round and round.
WHIZZ, WHIZZ, FIZZ, WHIRR!

The stone hit Goliath
straight between the eyes.
ZIP, ZAP, ZOOM, ZOOM!
He stood, swaying slightly,
then fell down in surprise.
ZIP, ZAP, TOTTER, BOOM!

David hurried to Goliath
to check that he was dead.
PUFF, PANT, PROD, OO-ER!
He picked up the giant's sword –
and chopped off his head!
SWISH, CHOP, SLICE, BLEUGH!

The Israelite army took their swords in hand,
ISRAEL, ISRAEL, WE'RE THE BEST!
And chased the losers out of their land!
DON'T CARE NOTHING FOR THE REST!

Now David was a hero,
you could hear the people sing
SHEPHERD, SOLDIER, SLING and SWORD
Of a giant-killing shepherd
who one day would be king.
"GOD IS GREAT! PRAISE THE LORD!"

Ready to tell

Oh no! Some of the pictures from this story have been mixed up! Can you retell the story and point to each picture in the correct order?

Picture dictionary

Encourage your child to read these harder words from the story and gradually develop their basic vocabulary.

armour

giant

helmet

king

sling

soldiers

stone

sword

tent

I • up • look • we • like • and • on • at • for •

Key words

Here are some key words used in context. Help your child to use other words from the border in simple sentences.

Goliath was **big**.

"**I** will fight him," said David.

He threw a stone **up** in the air.

"**Look!**" shouted David.

The soldiers ran **away**.

a • he • is • said • go • you • are • this • going • they • away • play • cat • to

day • get • come • in • went • was • of • me • she • see • it • yes • can • am

• the • dog • big • my • mum • no • dad • all •

Right on target!

Here's how to make a paper plane that should reach its destination as accurately as David's slingshot stones.

You will need

1 sheet of A4 paper • several paperclips

What to do

1 You need to work at a table or desk.

2 Fold the paper in half lengthwise to make a crease, then open it out again.

3 Lay the paper on the table with the short edge at the top. Carefully fold the top right-hand corner to the middle. Do the same with the top left-hand corner.

4 Fold the paper along the middle crease again. Keep the triangles you have made on the outside. Now the plane has a "nose" and "wings".

5 Fold one wing (or long edge of the paper) to make a parallel crease about 2cm above the middle crease. Repeat with the other wing.

6 Open out the wings, bending the back up slightly.

7 Add a couple of paperclips to the nose.

8 Take aim, and gently throw the plane forwards. Add another paperclip to the nose or change the amount you bend up the back of each wing to adjust its flight.